Mapping Skills

Grades 4-6

Written by Ruth Solski
Illustrated by Ric Ward

ISBN 1-55035-145-1
Copyright 1990
Revised January 2006
All Rights Reserved * Printed in Canada

Published in the United States by:
On the Mark Press
3909 Witmer Road PMB 175
Niagara Falls, New York
14305
www.onthemarkpress.com

Published in Canada by:
S&S Learning Materials
15 Dairy Avenue
Napanee, Ontario
K7R 1M4
www.sslearning.com

At a Glance™

Learning Expectations	Mapping Skills Booklet				Activity Cards		
	What is a Map?	Kinds of Maps	Map Symbols	Day & Night, Seasons	Basic Mapping Skills	Wold Mapping Skills	Mapping Word Study
Understanding Concepts							
• Become familiar with the types of maps used to identify different aspects of a country		●					
• Identify the four hemispheres and locate them on a globe or map			●				
• Understand the causes and effects of day and night, and the seasons			●	●			
• Locate and identify objects, and give directions in their environment using the cardinal and intermediate directions					●		
• Have a good understanding of, and use meridians of longitude and parallels of latitude to describe location			●			●	
Map anb Globe Skills							
• Locate and identify features on a map using the cardinal and intermediate directions					●	●	
• Use maps and the globe to locate countries, places, and physical features	●					●	
• Read maps by using the symbols listed in a legend or key					●	●	
• Create sketch maps of familiar places, using symbols for places and routes					●		
• Use number and letter grids to locate places					●	●	
• Measure distances using a scale					●		
Communication Skills							
• Use appropriate vocabulary and terms while reading and making maps	●	●	●	●	●	●	●

Mapping Skills

Table of Contents

At A Glance™ 2

Teacher Assessment Rubric 4

Student Self-Assessment Rubric 5

Preliminary Preparations 6

Introduction Ideas 6

Bulletin Board Ideas 7

Teacher Input Suggestions 7

Glossary of Geographic Terms 8

Teacher Information 12

Mapping Skills Booklet 16

Basic Mapping Skills Activity Cards 1 - 20 30

World Mapping Skills Activity Cards 1 - 10 45

Mapping Word Study Activities 60

Answer Key 62

 # Mapping Skills

Teacher Assessment Rubric

Student's Name: _____

Criteria	Level 1	Level 2	Level 3	Level 4	Level
Understanding Concepts					
• Understands the concepts introduced.	A few	Some	Most	All/almost all	
• Gives complete explanations independently without relying on teacher prompts.	Rarely	Sometimes	Usually	Always/almost always	
Map and Globe Skills					
• Successfully applies required skills.	A few	Some	Most	All/almost all	
• Applies skills independently without teacher assistance.	Rarely	Sometimes	Usually	Always/almost always	
Communication Skills					
• Uses correct mapping and globe vocabulary introduced.	Rarely	Sometimes	Usually	Always/almost always	
• Communicates clearly, accurately, and with details.	Rarely	Sometimes	Usually	Always/almost always	

Comments: _____

_____

_____

_____

_____

_____

_____

Mapping Skills
Student Self-Assessment Rubric

Name: _____ Date: _____

Put a check mark in each box that most accurately describes your performance, then add your points to determine your total score.

Expectations	Actual Performance (measured in points)				
	1 - Needs Improvement	2 - Sometimes	3 - Frequently	4 - Always/almost always	Points
Understanding Concepts					
I successfully identified, described, and explained the concepts introduced by my teacher.					
I gave complete explanations of concepts, independently without assistance from my teacher.					
Map and Globe Skills					
I read, used, and made maps correctly using symbols, grids, and the cardinal and intermediate directions.					
I read, used, and made maps accurately on my own without requiring help from my teacher or classmates.					
Communication Skills					
I used the correct vocabulary when talking and writing about a subject.					
I was clear, accurate, and gave lots of detail when I talked and wrote about a subject, and when I made maps.					

Total Points: _____

Questions for personal reflection:

1. What did you find most interesting, and enjoy learning about the most?

2. What questions do you have now, and what would you like to learn more about?

3. What can you improve upon, and how can you make this improvement?

 # Mapping Skills

Preliminary Preparations

Collect the following items well in advance of the unit: a large wall map of the world; a large wall map of North America; several globes; compasses; atlases; books pertaining to maps and mapping, road maps of your province or state; different types of maps that show physical features, vegetation areas, mineral resources, types of industries, populated areas, location of animal life, climate, political divisions; local maps; transit maps; railroad maps; community maps; school maps; puzzle maps; old maps; nautical charts; reproducible maps for student usage; walking tours; films; filmstrips; videos; computer games. In addition, make Cardinal Direction Cards and post them in your classroom for all to see and use.

Introduction Ideas

1. Before beginning this book, make sure that your students are familiar with the cardinal and intermediate directions found on a compass and a compass rose. Ask your students if they could give oral directions to the location of their home, their school or another street in their neighborhood. If they are not familiar with the cardinal and intermediate directions, take them outside at noon on a sunny day. Make sure that you have chosen a well lit spot in the playground. Have the students spread out so that they have room to stretch their arms out to the side without touching one another. Once the students are in position, have them note in which direction their shadow is pointing. The students are to stand in that direction. Tell your students that their shadow always points to the north at noon in North America.

   Give the following directions:

   a) Raise your right arm and point to the right. This direction is east.
   b) Raise you left arm and point in the opposite direction. Your left arm is now pointing west.
   c) Look behind you to find south.

2. Play games with your students such as "Simon Says" or have them move about in different directions. Play "I Spy" and have the students use the directions so others can locate the object that is seen by the student.

3. Display different types of maps and books that pertain to maps on a display table, and allow the students to peruse the articles a week in advance of the book.

4. Locate a good poem that pertains to a map, globe or traveling around the world. Record the poem on a chart and have the students read it.

5. Locate a good adventure story to a far off land to read to your students. Have them locate the country on the map of the world.

6. Blindfold a student. Have a second student lead him or her from point A to point B. Keep the path simple, with only one or two turns at the most.

   e.g. **A** chair
   chair
   table **B = 13 steps**

   Return the blindfolded student to point A. The student must then duplicate the path as closely as possible.

   Skills: counting step, noting turns, following directions that are not visual.

 # Mapping Skills

Bulletin Board Ideas

1. On a bulletin board display an historical map and a modern map. Discuss the maps with your students and compare them.

2. Display different types of maps for one country (preferably your own) in an interesting manner on the bulletin board. If you have access to an atlas that is falling apart, tear out the maps, mount them on a sturdy backing and laminate them. Print the name of the type of map on a label card and pin it near the map. For example: Physical Features, Vegetation, Location of Population, Mineral Resources, Political Map, etc.

3. Display a large map of your city, town or local community. The students may locate symbols that represent features on the map legend. They may also locate streets, buildings, parks, etc. This map may also be used to strengthen cardinal and intermediate directions.

4. Locate a large wall map of the world. Use pictures of famous world landmarks and have the students locate where they are found on the map. For example: Statue of Liberty - New York City, New York State, U.S.A.; CN Tower - Toronto, Ontario, Canada; Eiffel Tower - Paris, France; Buckingham Palace - London, England.

Teacher Input Suggestions

1. Use the reproducible booklet to teach the various aspects that pertain to maps and globes. Discuss the following topics and complete the work sheet page in the booklet as a follow-up to the lesson.

2. The information included in the unit will help to provide you with material on the topic. This information may be reproduced and given to the students to read along with the teacher, or it may be put on overheads and read with the entire class.

3. Discuss the following topics:
   a) What is a map?
   b) Why are maps important?
   c) What do maps tell us?
   d) Who makes maps?
   e) Kinds of maps
   f) Directional indicators
   g) Map symbols
   h) A legend or key
   i) Scale and measuring distance
   j) What is a globe? Why is it important? How are globes used?
   k) Hemispheres
   l) Lines on a globe - Parallels of latitude and meridians of longitude
   m) Day and night
   n) The seasons

4. The reproducible work sheets may be used as activity cards or reproduced for student usage. The activities are to be completed after all the content has been taught to reinforce many of the skills required to develop accurate map reading.

5. The Basic Map Reading Skills Cards (p. 30) should be used before the World Map Reading Skills Cards (p.45) if your students do not have any background knowledge or experience working with mapping skills. The Basic Map Reading Skills Cards may also be used as a review of the previously learned skills.

6. Some of the cards may be worked on independently while others would be better used in a large group setting to help students who are experiencing difficulty.

Glossary of Geographic Terms

altitude: the height or elevation above sea level.

Antarctic Circle: an imaginary line of latitude 66° 30' (66 degrees 30 minutes) south of the equator.

aphelion: the time of year when the earth is farthest from the sun.

archipelago: a group or chain of islands.

Arctic Circle: an imaginary line of latitude 66° 30' north of the equator.

atlas: a book of maps that represents the many areas of the earth's surface. It may also include maps of the other planets within the solar system.

axis: the diameter upon which the earth rotates.

bay: a part of an ocean, sea, or lake extending into land.

bank: the sloping ground bordering a stream, lake or other body of water; a shallow part of the ocean.

basin: a depression or hollow which may or may not contain water, surrounded by higher land.

brook: a small, natural stream of fresh water.

canal: a narrow, man-made waterway used for ships or irrigation.

canyon: a deep, narrow valley with steep, sloping sides.

cape (or point): a point of land extending into a body of water.

cardinal directions: the four compass directions – north, south, east and west – which are read along the meridians and parallels on the globe.

channel: a narrow passage of water between two land masses that connects two large bodies of water; also the deepest part of a river or harbor.

cliff: a steep, high wall of rock along a coast, river or lake.

coast: the land bordering the sea, the seashore.

compass directions: the directions away from any given place based upon magnetic north.

compass rose: the design which shows the directions on a map; the north and south "petals" are usually longer than the east, west and intermediate "petals".

 # Mapping Skills

continent: any one of the earth's seven large land masses such as North America, South America, Europe, Asia, Africa, Australia, Antarctica.

contour map: a map that uses contour lines to show land that is uneven; the space between the lines indicates the steepness of the slope of the land.

day: the approximate time for one rotation of the earth - 24 hours.

degree: one of the 360 units of measurement which make up a circle, represented by the symbol °. Degrees are subdivided into 60 minutes, represented by the symbol'.

delta: a triangular or fan-shaped area of soil that has been carried downstream and dropped at a river's mouth.

depression: a land area that is lower than the surrounding ground. A depression is often below sea level.

desert: a land area so dry that little or no plant life will grow. Very few people live in a desert.

diameter: a line passing through the center of a sphere.

distortion: the stretching or compressing of parts of a map when it is transferred from the globe to a flat plane.

down: toward the center of the earth.

east: the direction along a parallel toward the rising sun.

eastern hemisphere: the half of the earth that includes Africa, Asia, Australia, Europe and their waters.

elevation: the height or distance above sea level.

equator: an imaginary line of latitude (0°), halfway between the North and South Poles.

equinoxes: the two times of the year, usually about March 21 and September 21, when the sun's rays are perpendicular to the equator, and day and night are of equal length everywhere.

glacier: a large body of ice that moves slowly down a mountainside or along a valley toward sea level.

globe: the only true world map, made on a ball or sphere the shape of the earth.

Greenwich meridian: the meridian passing through the borough of Greenwich in London, England, now used as 0° longitude (the prime meridian) from which time around the world is calculated.

grid: the network of meridians and parallels on a map.

gulf: a large arm of an ocean or sea partly surrounded by land.

hemisphere: any half of the earth's surface.

highland: a high or hilly point of land.

hill: a slightly higher point of land rising above the surrounding land.

horizon: the line where the earth's surface and the sky seem to meet.

ice shelf: a thick, floating area of ice lying next to a land area.

Mapping Skills

intermediate directions: the directions on the compass which fall between two of the cardinal directions; northeast, southeast, southwest, northwest.

island: an area of land, smaller than a continent, completely surrounded by water.

isthmus: a narrow strip of land located between two water bodies, connecting two large land areas.

International Date Line: an imaginary line of longitude generally 180° east or west of the prime meridian. The date becomes one day earlier to the east of the line.

lagoon: a shallow area of water separated from the ocean by a sandbank or by a strip of low land.

lake: a body of fresh or salt water entirely surrounded by land.

land hemisphere: the hemisphere with the maximum land area, roughly centered on northern France.

latitude: the distance, measured in degrees, north or south of the equator.

longitude: the distance, measured in degrees, east or west of the prime meridian.

map: a drawing of all or a part of the earth.

meridian: an imaginary line of longitude running between the North Pole and the South Pole.

minute: one of 60 equal parts of a degree.

mountain: an unusually high elevation rising steeply above its surroundings.

north: the directions along a meridian toward the North Pole and North Star.

North Pole: the point farthest north on the earth's surface. It is 90° north of the equator.

northern hemisphere: the half of the earth's surface north of the equator.

oasis: a spot in a desert made fertile by the presence of water.

ocean: one of the large areas of the earth into which the water surface is divided.

orbit of the earth: the path of the earth as it revolves around the sun.

parallel: a latitude line running east and west around the earth parallel to the equator.

peak: the highest point of a mountain.

peninsula: a piece of land extending into the sea almost completely surrounded by water.

perihelion: the time of the year when the earth is closest to the sun.

plain: a flat or level area of land.

plateau: an elevated area of mostly level land, sometimes containing deep canyons.

population: the number of people or inhabitants living in a country, a city or town, or a particular area.

prime meridian: the zero meridian from which east and west longitude are measured, passing through London (Greenwich).

range: a group or chain of high elevations.

reef: a chain of coral rocks or ridge of sand lying at or near the surface of a body of water.

reservoir: a man-made lake where water is kept for future use.

revolution: the movement of the earth in its orbit around the sun, or the moon around the earth.

river: a large stream of water which flows on the earth's surface.

scale: the numerical relationship between an actual distance on the earth and the distance which represents it on a map.

sea: a large body of salt water smaller than an ocean.

sea level: the surface level of the oceans. It is the same all over the world.

seasons: the divisions of the year – spring, summer, autumn, winter – determined by the position of the earth in relation to the sun.

solstices: the times of the year, about June 21 and December 22, when the sun's rays reach their northern and southern limits at the tropic lines.

source: the place of origin of a river or stream.

south: the directions along a meridian toward the South Pole.

South Pole: the point farthest south on the earth's surface. It is 90° south of the equator.

southern hemisphere: the half of the earth's surface south of the equator.

symbol: a drawing, letter, or figure that represents a feature or idea.

strait: a narrow body of water connecting two larger bodies of water.

swamp: a low area of wet, spongy ground.

topographic map: a map that shows the detailed surface features, both natural and cultural, of a small area.

tributary: a river or stream that flows into a larger stream or other body of water.

Tropic of Cancer: an imaginary line of latitude 23° 30' north of the equator.

Tropic of Capricorn: an imaginary line of latitude 23° 30' south of the equator.

up: away from the center of the earth toward a point directly overhead.

valley: a long, narrow, land area lying between two areas of higher elevation. A valley usually contains a river or stream.

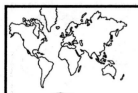

vegetation: all the different kinds of plant life that grow on the earth's surface.

volcano: a cone-shaped mountain that has an opening in the earth's crust from which lava can flow.

waterfall: a sudden drop of a stream from a high level to a much lower level.

water hemisphere: the hemisphere with the maximum water area, roughly centered at 40° S. latitude and 179° W. longitude.

west: the direction along a parallel toward the setting sun.

western hemisphere: the half of the earth that includes North America, South America and their waters.

year: the time required for one revolution of the earth around the sun.

Teacher Information

What is a Map?

A map is a drawn or printed representation of the earth or any other heavenly body. Most maps are flat, although some have raised surfaces. A *globe* is also a map in the shape of a sphere.

Maps provide information through lines, colors, shapes, and symbols. The symbols represent such features as rivers, lakes, roads, and cities. The features on a map are greatly reduced in size. The distance of 160 kilometers (100 miles) might be represented by 2.5 centimeters (1 inch) on a map.

Maps are used to locate places, measure distances, plan trips, and find our way. Pilots of ships and airplanes use maps to navigate. Maps provide us with information about a place, such as climate, population, and transportation routes. Some maps show such patterns as where people live and how they use the land.

Through the years, people have explored more of the world and have added new information to maps. Scientific discoveries have made maps more accurate. Today, most maps are based on photographs taken from the air. The making and study of maps is called *cartography*. The maker of a map, or someone who studies maps, is called a *cartographer*.

Types of Maps

There are many types of maps. The most common ones are *general reference maps, mobility maps,* *thematic maps* and *inventory maps*.

General reference maps identify and locate various geographic features. They may include land features, bodies of water, political boundaries, cities and towns, roads and many other elements. General reference maps are used to locate specific places and to observe their location in relation to other places. Examples of general reference maps are maps of provinces, states, countries, and continents. These maps are usually found in atlases.

A *political map* is one that emphasizes the boundaries of counties, provinces, states and countries. *Physical maps* or *terrain maps* emphasize the location of physical features found on the earth's surface such as mountains, rivers and lakes.

Mobility maps are created to help people find their way from one place to another. There are mobility maps for travel on land, on water, or in the air. Maps that are used to navigate ships and planes are called *charts*.

The most common mobility map is a *road map*. A road map represents different types of roads such as divided highways, four-lane roads, major routes and scenic routes. It also shows the location of cities, towns, provincial and state parks, and other places connected by these roads. Travelers use road maps to plan trips and to follow lengthy routes.

A *street map* is similar to a road map. It shows a much smaller area in much greater detail. This type of map is used to locate specific addresses and to plan and follow short routes.

Transit maps show the routes of buses, subways, and other systems of public transportation in cities and towns. These maps help people reach their destination by means of public transportation.

Aeronautical charts are maps used to navigate airplanes. Pilots of small, low-flying aircraft plan and follow a course by using *VFR charts* (visual flight rules charts) . VFR charts show such landmarks as bridges, highways, railroad tracks, rivers and towns. These charts also show the location of airports, the heights of *mountains and other obstructions. Pilots of low-flying airplanes and crews of high-flying aircraft use IFR charts* (instrument flight rules charts). These charts are designed for radio navigation. IFR charts locate transmitters that beam very high radio frequency signals, which help pilots and airplane crews to determine their position and course.

Nautical charts are maps used to navigate ships and boats. They show the depths of water, the location of lighthouses, buoys, islands, and dangers such as coral reefs and underwater mountains that come close to the surface. Nautical charts also locate the source of radio signals that navigators use to determine their course and position.

Thematic Maps

A *thematic map* shows the distribution of a particular feature such as population, rainfall or a natural resource. This type of map is used to study an overall pattern. A thematic map may show where wheat is produced in North America or how the average rainfall varies from one part of a country to another. Quantities are expressed on thematic maps through the use of symbols or colors.

Inventory Maps

Inventory maps are similar to thematic maps in the way that they concentrate on a specific feature. These maps show the precise location of the specific feature. A map showing every building in a community is an example of an inventory map.

Mapping Skills

Reading a Map

In order to read a map, one must understand *map legends, scale, geographic grids* and *map indexes.*

A *map legend* lists and explains the symbols and colors found on a map. Sometimes the map symbols do resemble the features that they represent. For example, a tree-shaped symbol may represent a forest or an orchard. Many symbols have no resemblance to what they represent at all. For example a circle or large dot may represent where a city stands or it may represent where a group of homes can be found. It is very important to read the map legend to find out what the symbols mean. Most maps are printed to show north at the top. Most map legends include an arrow that indicates which direction is north.

Scale

The *scale* on a map shows the relationship between distances on the map and the corresponding distances on the earth's surface. Scale is shown on a straight line with distances marked off on a *bar scale.* A bar scale is like a ruler or measuring tape. You can measure long distances with a bar scale. Each mark represents a certain number of miles or kilometers.

Some maps indicate scale in words and figures. The scale might appear as 2.5 centimeters = 10 kilometers (1 inch = 6 miles). In other words 2.5 centimeters (1 inch) represents a distance of 10 kilometers (6 miles) on the earth's surface.

Geographic Grids

Geographic grids are lines on maps that help us find and describe locations. The most common grid uses the east-west lines, called *parallels*, and the north-south lines, called *meridians.* The parallel lines and the *meridians form the graticule.*

Parallels are lines that encircle the globe from *east* to *west.* The parallel that lies exactly halfway between the North and South Pole is called the *equator.* Parallels are used to measure *latitude.* They measure distance from the equator toward either pole. Latitude is measured in *degrees of a circle.* Any point on the equator has a latitude of zero degrees, written "0°". The North Pole has a latitude of 90° north and the South Pole has a latitude of 90° south. Parallels are sometimes called *lines of latitude.*

Meridians are lines that extend halfway around the globe from the North Pole to the South Pole. Mapmakers *count meridians from the line that passes through Greenwich, England, a borough of London. The Greenwich* meridian is also known as the *prime meridian.* Meridians measure longitude, which is the distance east or west of the prime meridian. *Longitude* is measured in degrees of a circle too. Meridians run from 0° at Greenwich to 180°. The 180° meridian lies halfway around the world from the Prime Meridian. Meridians are sometimes *called lines of longitude.*

Longitude and latitude are used to pinpoint places around the world.

Map Indexes

A *map index* helps us to locate places on a map. The features shown on a map are listed in alphabetical order in the index. At the back of most atlases, an index is found. Each entry in the index is listed with its longitude and latitude.

Mapping Skills

Some maps are divided into horizontal rows and vertical columns by an index grid. Letters are often used along the sides of the map to label the horizontal lines. Numbers are used across the top and bottom of the map to label the vertical rows. In this case, each entry in the map index is followed by a letter and a number corresponding to a row and a column on the map. This feature is found where the row and column cross.

Hemispheres

A *hemisphere* is one-half of a sphere. The word *hemisphere* is the name given to any half of the globe. It comes from the Greek word that means *half a sphere*. The world is divided into four main hemispheres. They are: 1) the northern and southern hemispheres, 2) the eastern and western hemispheres, 3) land and water hemispheres, and 4) daylight and darkness hemispheres.

The *northern and southern hemispheres* share the equator as a boundary line. All areas north of the equator make up the northern hemisphere. All areas south of the equator make up the southern hemisphere.

The *eastern and western hemispheres* have no natural dividing line such as the Equator. The eastern hemisphere, or "Old World", is made up of the continents of *Europe, Asia, Africa* and *Australia*. The western hemisphere, or "New World", is made up of the continents of *North America* and *South America*.

The earth is also divided as a *land hemisphere* and a *water hemisphere*. The land hemisphere includes half of the earth with the *most land*. Its center lies near London, England. The other half of the earth is mostly water and makes up the water hemisphere. Its center lies near New Zealand.

During a day, one half of the earth is in *darkness* and the other is in *light*. The earth is also separated into a *daylight* and *darkness hemispheres*. There is no sharp boundary between the daylight and darkness hemispheres. They are separated by the *twilight zones of dawn and dusk*. At the same time, they are continually changing their position on the surface of the earth as it rotates on its axis.

Directional Indicators

Most maps have a symbol called a *compass rose*. The purpose of the compass rose is to show the cardinal directions: *North, South, East, West*. Some compass roses have only four lines, called *petals*. Some directional indicators may only show "N" for North.

Sometimes a compass rose will have more than four directions. These are called the intermediate directions. The *intermediate petals* fall between two of the cardinal directions. They are called *northeast,* southeast, northwest, and *southwest*. One way to remember direction is with the word *"WE"*: West is on the left and East in on the right.

If a compass rose is not found on the map, the *top* of the map is usually *north*.

Map Symbols

One way to show features on a map is to create *symbols* that represent them. A symbol is a shape or pattern that represents an object. Symbols and their meanings are shown on a *key* or *legend* on the map.

Mapping Skills

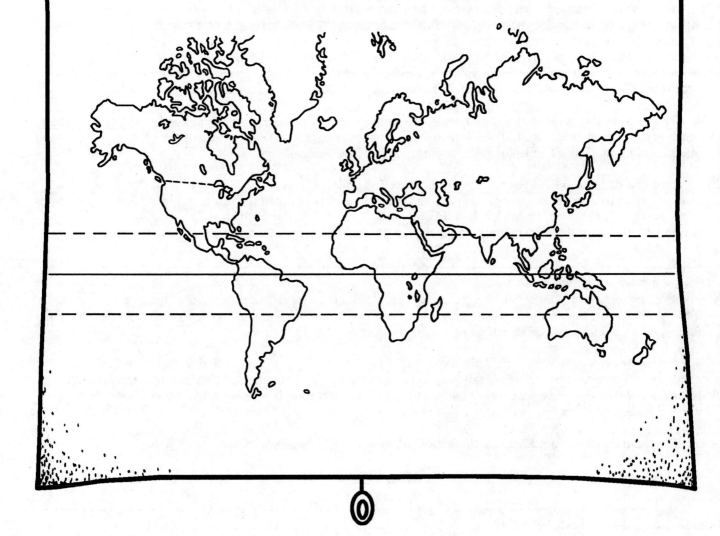

Name: _____

 # Mapping Skills

What is a Map?

Use the words in the box to complete the sentences which follow.

flat	roads	continent	map
buildings	trees	earth	picture
water	land	city	world
country	picture	diagram	

A _____ is like a _____ of the _____ taken from high up in the air or from space. A map is a _____ of a _____, _____, _____ or the _____.

Maps can show _____ and _____ areas found on the earth. Many things that are located upon the land areas such as _____, _____ and _____ are shown on maps. Most maps are _____.

This is a map of British Columbia.

1. Color the land *green*

2. Color the water *blue*.

3. In which country would you find British Columbia?

    _____

4. On which coast is British Columbia found?

    _____

5. In which continent is British Columbia found?

    _____

6. Which land areas border British Columbia?

    _____

    _____

Mapping Skills

1. Why are maps important, and what are they used for?

   _____
   _____
   _____
   _____
   _____
   _____

2. What types of information can one gain from different types of maps of a country? Certain maps tell us:

   _____
   _____
   _____
   _____
   _____
   _____
   _____
   _____
   _____
   _____

3. What is cartography?

   _____
   _____

4. What is a cartographer?

   _____
   _____

Kinds of Maps

1. There are many types of maps used today and for a variety of reasons. The most common ones are:

   a) _____
   b) _____
   c) _____

Mapping Skills

General Reference Maps

2. General reference maps may show:

a) _____

b) _____

c) _____

d) _____

Examples of general reference maps are:

a) _____

b) _____

c) _____

d) _____

3. Where are general reference maps found?

_____

4. What is a political map?

_____

_____

5. What is a physical or relief map?

_____

_____

Mobility Maps

1. What is a mobility map?

_____

_____

2. How are mobility maps used?

_____

_____

3. What is a chart?

_____

_____

4. Who uses charts?

_____

_____

Mapping Skills

5. Which type of mobility map is the most common?

_____

_____

_____

6. What elements are found on a road map?

_____

_____

_____

7. Name other types of mobility maps.

_____   _____

_____   _____

_____   _____

Thematic Maps

1. What is a thematic map?

_____

_____

_____

Some types of thematic maps show:

_____   _____

_____   _____

_____   _____

Inventory Maps

1. What is an inventory map?

_____

_____

_____

Example:

_____

_____

_____

Mapping Skills

Directional Indicators

Part A:

A _____ is an instrument that shows which _____ we are facing or traveling. An ordinary compass is a _____, _____ box with a _____ inside it. The needle always points _____.

In this drawing of a compass, the arrows point to these directions: _____, _____, _____ and _____. These directions are called _____ directions or the cardinal _____, of the compass.

Between each cardinal direction there is an _____ direction.

The intermediate directions are _____, _____, _____ and _____.

Complete the following activity.

a) On the drawing of the compass, mark a point on the circle about halfway between the words *north* and *east*. Draw a straight line from the center of the circle to that point. Label the point NE. Those letters stand for the word _____. It is the name of the direction halfway between _____ and _____.

b) Draw a straight line from the center of the circle to a point on the circle halfway between the words *south* and *east*. Label that point SE, the abbreviation for the word _____.

c) Draw a straight line from the center of the circle to a point halfway between the words *north* and *west*. Label it NW, which stands for _____.

d) Draw a straight line from the center of the circle to a point halfway between the words *south* and *west*. Label it SW, which stands for _____.

Part B:

A _____ usually has a symbol called a _____ _____.

Below are some examples.

 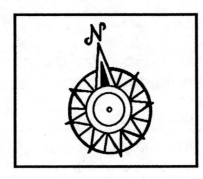 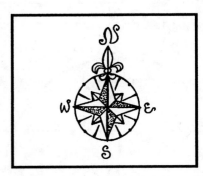

The purpose of the compass rose is to show the _____ directions: _____(N), _____(E), _____(S), _____(W).

Some compass roses just show N for _____. Directly below north is _____, to the right is _____ and to the left is _____.

Label the following compass rose by printing the cardinal and intermediate directions on it. Beside each abbreviation write the full word on the line.

1. N = _____
2. E = _____
3. SW = _____
4. NW = _____
5. SE = _____
6. NE = _____
7. S = _____
8. W = _____

If a compass rose is not on a map, the _____ of the map is usually _____.

Mapping Skills

Map Symbols

A _____ "stands for something". Mapmakers use small _____ or

symbols to stand for different things when they make their _____. The symbol

often looks like or suggests the feature it _____.

Example:

You can _____ recognize what each symbol represents.

Legend	
🏫	school
⛪	church
🏠	house
🌳	tree
═══	highway
───	road

A map usually has a _____ or a

_____. A key is the _____ that

_____ the door to reading the map. The

symbols are contained in a _____.

Mapping Skills

Map Symbols Used in Atlases

The symbols below are ones frequently seen on most maps. Label each one neatly.

1. ---·---·--- _____

2. --·--·-- _____

3. ⭐ _____

4. ◎ _____

5. ●■▬ _____

6. _____

7. _____

8. ▲ _____

9.)(_____

10. _____

11. _____

12. _____

13. _____

14. _____

15. _____

16. _____

17. _____

18. _____

19. _____

20. _____

A Map Tells Distance

A map can be used to tell distance when it has a _____ _____.

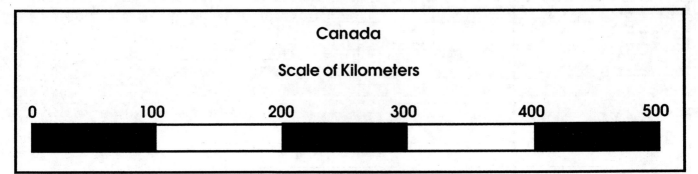

Canada

Scale of Kilometers

| 0 | 100 | 200 | 300 | 400 | 500 |

Mapping Skills

A bar scale is like a _____ or _____. You can measure
_____ distances with a bar scale.

What does "scale" mean?

_____

_____

Maps are _____ _____ or plans of places. A map of a country, a city,
or even a room could be too _____ to use if it were drawn to exactly the
same size as the place really is. Mapmakers let a small length such as a
_____ stand for a _____ or a _____.

What is a Globe?

Use the words in the box to complete the following sentences about the globe.

shapes	**lands**	**positions**	**stand**	**world**
seas	**triangular**	**earth**	**map**	**terrestrial**
globe	**sphere**	**gores**	**printed**	**spin**
pasted	**world map**	**roundness**	**rotates**	

A _____ is a model of the _____. It shows the
_____ of our _____. A globe is mounted on a
_____ so that it can _____ showing how the earth
_____ as it travels around the sun.

A globe is a _____ that has been _____ or _____
on a hollow _____. Globes of the earth are called _____
globes.

They are made of a series of _____ strips of
material called _____. The gores are pasted
on a sphere and a _____ is printed on the gores.

A globe shows all the _____ and _____
in their true _____ and _____.

Mapping Skills

How are Globes Used?

1. How are globes used?

_____

_____

2. Why is a globe important?

_____

_____

_____

Hemispheres

1. What is a hemisphere?

_____

_____

2. Into how many hemispheres is the globe divided?

_____

_____

3. What are the four hemispheres called?

_____   _____

_____   _____

The Northern and Southern Hemispheres

The northern and southern hemispheres share the _____ as a _____ line. All areas _____ of the equator make up the _____ hemisphere. All the areas _____ of the equator make up the _____ hemisphere.

A)

_____

_____

B)

_____

_____

Mapping Skills

The Eastern and Western Hemispheres

The eastern and western hemispheres do not have a _____ _____
_____. The eastern hemisphere is made up of the continents of _____,
_____, _____ and _____. The western hemisphere is
made up of the continents of _____ _____ and _____
_____.

A)   _____   B)   _____

Land and Water Hemispheres

The land hemisphere includes the _____ of the earth with the _____
land. Its center lies near _____, _____. The other half of the earth
is mainly _____. This makes up the _____ _____.
Its center lies near _____.

Daylight and Darkness Hemispheres

During one day, one half of the earth is in _____ and one half is in
_____. There is no definite _____ _____ between the
daylight and darkness hemispheres. These hemispheres are separated by the
_____ zones of _____ and _____. These
hemispheres are continually changing positions on the earth's surface as it
_____ on its axis.

Lines on the Globe

_____ are _____ on maps that help us _____ and
describe locations.

The most common grid uses the east-west lines called _____ of _____
and the north-south lines called _____ or _____ of _____.

Mapping Skills

Each parallel of latitude runs _____ to _____ and describes the position of a point on the earth's surface in relation to the _____.

The latitude of a point is measured in _____ from the equator towards one of the _____ _____.

The _____ has a latitude of _____ _____ (written 0⁰). The North Pole has a latitude of _____ _____ and the South Pole has a latitude of _____ _____. _____ of latitude are divided into _____ minutes (') and the minutes each consist of 60 seconds (").

Lines of _____ or _____ begin in _____, a borough of London. Greenwich lies at 0⁰ longitude. This line of longitude is called the _____ _____. Lines of longitude are lines that run from the _____ to _____ on maps and globes to indicate distances and locate points. All the lines of longitude _____ at the North and South Poles. The distance between the meridians is greatest at the equator. This distance gradually _____ as the meridians (lines of longitude) near the poles.

Label the following parallels of latitude on the globe.

| Tropic of Cancer | Arctic Circle | North Pole | Equator |
| Tropic of Capricorn | Antartic Circle | South Pole | |

Parallels of Latitude

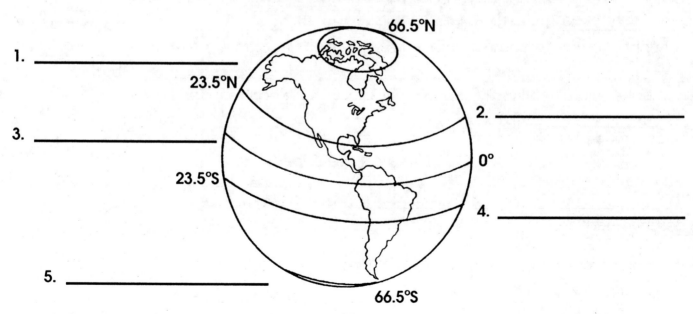

1. _____

2. _____

3. _____

4. _____

5. _____

Mapping Skills

Day and Night

A _____ day is the length of time that it takes the _____ to turn around once with respect to the sun. _____ refers to the time when the _____ is shining on our part of the earth. _____ refers to the time when our part of the earth is _____ or turned _____ from the sun.

Each day begins at _____ in most countries and the day is divided into _____ parts of _____ hours each. The hours from _____ to _____ are the _____ (before noon) hours. The hours from _____ to _____ are the _____ (after noon) hours.

The length of _____ changes during the year in all parts of the world. The _____ of the earth's _____ causes one _____ to _____ towards the sun and the other to slant away from the sun. When the earth's axis causes the _____ Pole to face the sun, the _____ Pole is continuously _____. As the North Pole tilts _____ from the sun, it becomes _____ while the South Pole has constant _____.

The Seasons

Each year the earth goes through _____ seasons. The seasons are _____, _____, _____ and _____. Each season lasts approximately _____ months and brings changes in _____, _____ and the _____.

During the spring, the days are _____ and get _____. Summers can be _____ during the day and _____ at night. In the autumn, days become _____ and begin to _____. During the winter it is _____ with much _____ days.

The _____ seasons are caused by the changing _____ of the earth in relation to the sun. When the _____ slants towards the sun, the _____ hemisphere receives the _____ sunlight and it is summer. When the North Pole slants away from the sun, the northern hemisphere receives the _____ sunlight and it is _____. Spring begins when the North Pole _____ to slant toward the sun and _____ begins when the North Pole starts to slant away again.

Summer begins in the northern hemisphere on _____ during the summer _____. The sun is high in the sky and this is the _____ day of the year. The _____ solstice marks the beginning of winter on _____ and this day is the _____ one of the year. The Vernal Equinox marks the beginning of _____ on _____. The Autumnal Equinox is the beginning of autumn which takes place on _____ or _____. During each equinox, places on the earth have approximately _____ hours of _____ and _____ hours of _____.

Mapping Skills

Basic Mapping Skills Card #1

Using a Directional Indicator

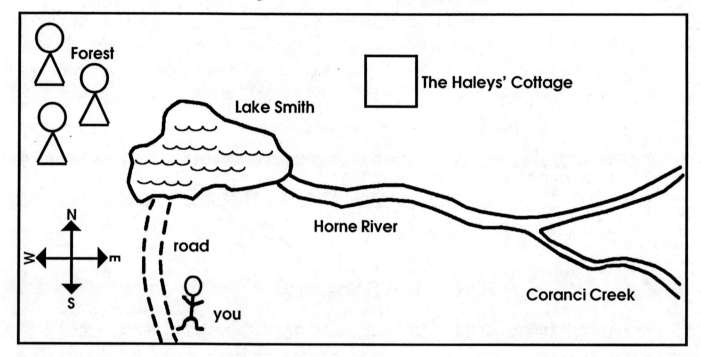

Maps give you a lot of information.

On this map there is a special symbol **N**. It is called a **directional indicator**. This symbol shows us where **north** is.

If **you** walk along the road, you are heading **north** and will soon be at Lake Smith.

Color Lake Smith, Horne River and Coranci Creek **blue**.

Color the road **brown**.

Color the Haleys' Cottage **yellow**.

Color the forest **green**.

Go over the directional indicator in **red**.

Mapping Skills

Basic Mapping Skills Card #2

Using a Directional Indicator

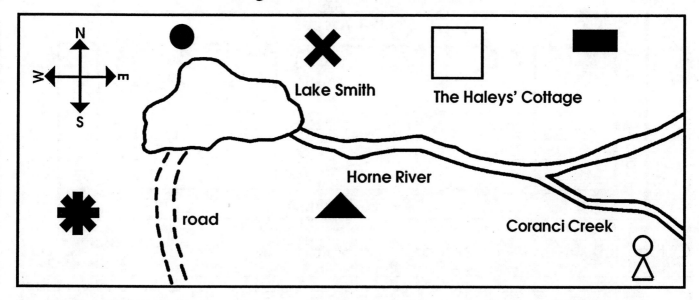

Some maps give a directional indicator showing north, south, east and west. This will help you to locate a place on the map and it will also tell someone else how to find it.

Example: "The Haleys' cottage is north of Horne River."
"The road is south of Lake Smith."

On the map are some symbols:

Complete these sentences using the words **north**, **south**, **west** or **east**.

1. The ✖ is _____ of the Haleys' cottage.
2. The ▬ is _____ of the Haley's cottage.
3. The ▲ is _____ of Horne River.
4. The ⚲ is _____ of Coranci River.
5. The ● is _____ of Smith Lake.
6. The ✳ is _____ of the _____ .

Basic Mapping Skills Card #3

Reading a Map

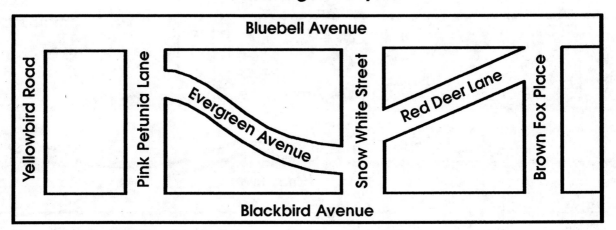

Color each street the color that is part of its name.

- -

Mapping Skills

Basic Mapping Skills Card #4

Reading a Map

Fill in the right direction.

North, South, East, West

1. Spirit Town is _____ of Ghost Town.

2. Dragon City is _____ of Ghost Town.

3. Monster Village is _____ of _____ and _____.

4. Gremlin City is _____ of Spirit Town.

5. Spirit Town is _____ of Gremlin City.

Mapping Skills

Basic Mapping Skills Card #5

Reading a Map

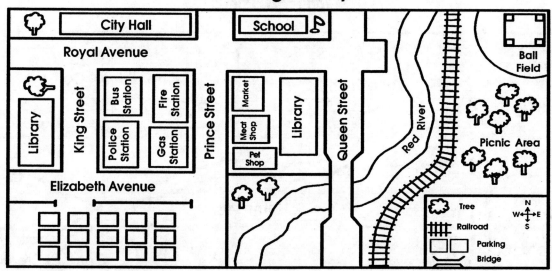

Complete each sentence below with the correct answer.

1. The ball field is _____ of the picnic area.

2. The school is found at the corner of _____ Street and _____ Street.

3. City Hall is located on _____.

4. Parking is available south of _____.

5. The railroad runs _____ and _____ and is located _____ of the Red River.

6. The _____ is found on Queen Street.

7. City Hall is located on _____.

8. Royal Avenue runs _____ and _____.

9. On Prince Street, you can shop for food at the _____ and the _____.

10. You can catch a bus at the corner of _____ Street and _____ Avenue.

Basic Mapping Skills Card #6

Map Symbols

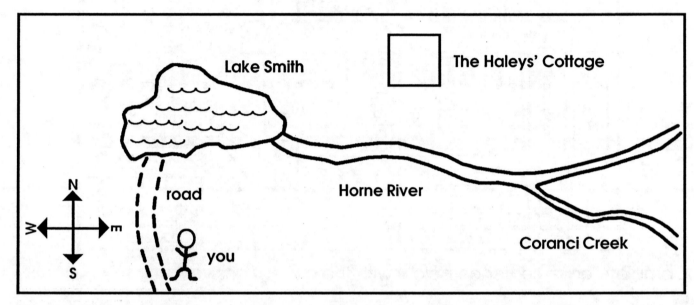

On the map above there are symbols that represent different features on it.

What does each symbol represent?

1. ▢ means _____

2. 〰 means _____

3. 〰 means _____

4. ·---· means _____

On the map above draw three trees west of the Haleys' cottage.

On the map above draw two trees south of the Horne River.

This symbol ooooooooooooooo will represent a path.

Make a path from the Haleys' cottage to the lake.

Color your map.

Mapping Skills

Basic Mapping Skills Card #7

Recognizing Map Symbols

Draw a line from the word to its map symbol.

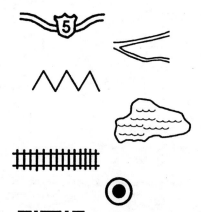

1. bridge
2. mountains
3. lake
4. boundary line
5. river
6. railroad
7. highway
8. city

Mapping Skills

Basic Mapping Skills Card #8

Using Map Symbols to Make a Map

On a large sheet of paper draw a map using these symbols.

Remember to put on a directional indicator.

 lake    forest    house   river

 church   bridge   road    railroad

Basic Mapping Skills Card #9

The Legend or Key

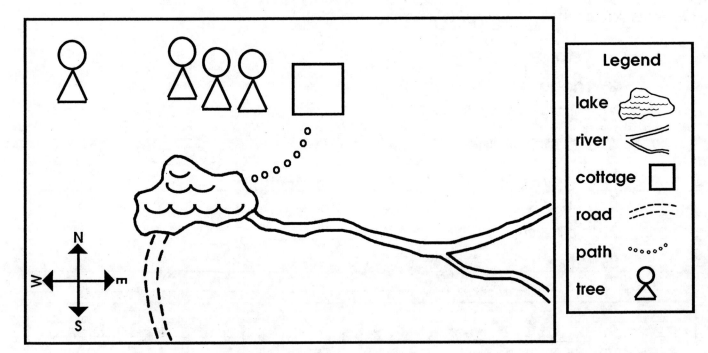

Most maps have a legend or key that helps you to read the map correctly.

Since the space on a map is limited, symbols are used instead of words.

The symbols are listed in a "legend" or "key".

The legend or key unlocks the code and tells you what the symbols represent.

Each symbol in a legend must match the color and shape of the symbol used on a map.

Color the legend's symbols.

Then color the same symbols on the map to match.

Mapping Skills

Basic Mapping Skills Card #10

Making a Map

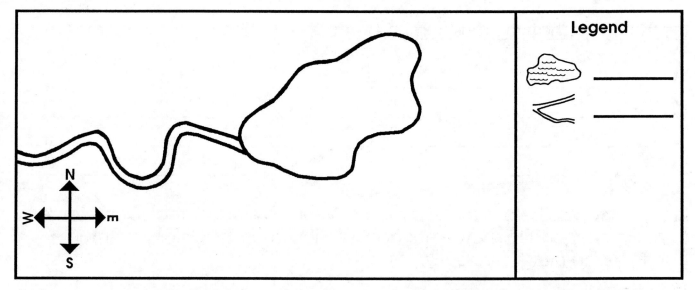

Above is a picture of Marty's Lake. Karen Creek runs into Marty's Lake.

Follow the directions below and complete the map and the legend.

1. Be sure to print in pencil.

2. Make symbols to match the underlined words in the information below. Put the symbols on the legend. Color each symbol.

   - Beth and Sandra live south of Marty's Lake in a **house**.
   - Bruce and Mike live in a **house** south of Karen Creek but right by the creek.
   - There is a **road** from Beth and Sandra's house to Bruce and Mike's house.
   - South of Beth and Sandra's house is a **school**.
   - North of the lake is a **store**.
   - There are **two trees** east of Bruce and Mike's house.

3. Place the symbols on the map to match the information given in the legend.

4. Color the symbols on the map to match those on the legend.

 # Mapping Skills

Basic Mapping Skills Card #11

Mapping Your Class!

List the things that you must remember to show when you make a map.

1. _____

2. _____

3. _____

4. _____

In the rectangle below, make a map of your classroom area. Don't forget to make a legend to show what each symbol means. **Color** your map carefully and **print** very neatly.

Map of My Classroom

	Legend

Mapping Skills

Basic Mapping Skills Card #12

Mapping My School Grounds

This is a map of Owain and Erich's school grounds. It shows us where the road, the playing field, the creek and the "climbers" are.

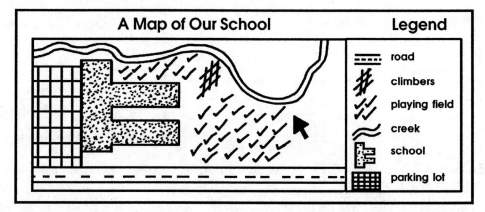

Make a map of your school grounds. Be sure to show the shape of your school.

Use symbols to represent things such as swings, playground equipment, the baseball diamond, climbers, basketball hoops, parking lot, playing field, etc.

Remember to:

1. Include a directional indicator and a legend.
2. Color your legend symbols and map symbols the same colors.
3. Use a pencil to draw your map and label it.

My School Grounds

	Legend

Mapping Skills

Basic Mapping Skills Card #13

Mapping Your Route to School

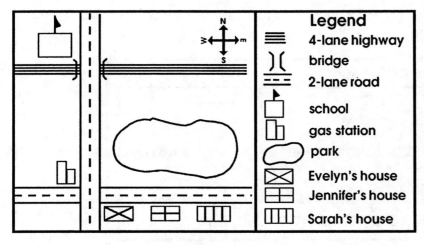

Evelyn, Jennifer and Sarah made a map of the route their bus takes to school each day.

They showed landmarks that would help someone to find his or her way and not get lost!

Landmarks are usually big buildings, parks, etc. that are easily noticed.

The girls only used a few symbols because they did not want to put too much information on the map. They showed only their homes.

Draw a map showing the best way to get from your house to the school. Only put on meaningful symbols.

Remember: 1. directional indicator   2. legend
3. use a pencil   4. symbols must match in color

My Route to School

	Legend

Mapping Skills

Basic Mapping Skills Card #14

Using a Scale to Find Distance

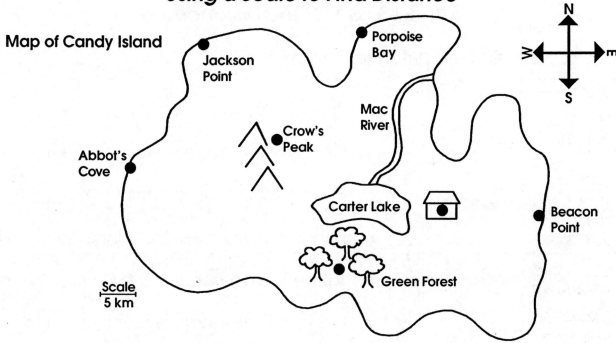

Map of Candy Island

Jackson Point

Porpoise Bay

Mac River

Crow's Peak

Abbot's Cove

Carter Lake

Beacon Point

Green Forest

Scale
5 km

N
W E
S

- The map of Candy Island has been "drawn to scale".

- On this map, drawing to scale means that one centimeter (cm) on the map equals five real kilometers (km).

- With a ruler, measure the distance from Abbot's Cove to Beacon Point. It is _____ cm long. Now multiply by five to find its distance in kilometers. The distance from Abbot's Cove to Beacon Point is _____ km.

Measure to find out the distances in kilometers

1. The distance from Crow's Peak to the house on Carter Lake is approximately _____ km.

2. From Porpoise Bay to Beacon Point is _____ km.

3. From Jackson Point to Porpoise Bay and then to the Green Forest is a total of _____ km.

4. To get from the Green Forest to Abbot's Cove by way of Crow's Peak is _____ km.

5. Using string, find the approximate distance all around Candy Island: _____ km.

 # Mapping Skills

Basic Mapping Skills Card #15

Using Scale to Find Distance

Use the scale to find the distance in kilometers.

Bubble City

Toffee Town

Candyville

Licorice Town •

• Popcorn Town

Peppermint City

Chocolate City

Scale
1 km

1. Bubble City to Candyville _____ km

2. Candyville to Toffee Town _____ km

3. Bubble City to Peppermint City _____ km

4. Popcorn Town to Peppermint City _____ km

5. Toffee Town to Chocolate City _____ km

6. Candyville to Licorice Town _____ km

- -

Basic Mapping Skills Card #16

Drawing to Scale

Draw a rectangle that is six meters long and four meters wide using the scale below.

Draw a square that is six meters on each side using the scale below.

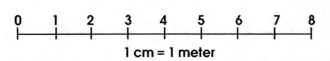

0 1 2 3 4 5 6 7 8

1 cm = 1 meter

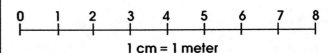

0 1 2 3 4 5 6 7 8

1 cm = 1 meter

Mapping Skills

Basic Mapping Skills Card #17

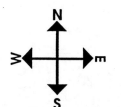

N-North
E-East
S-South
W-West

Using a Grid

Follow the instructions carefully.

1. From point A, draw a line north five spaces.
2. Travel east four spaces.
3. Go north three spaces.
4. Head east seven spaces.
5. Turn south three spaces.
6. Travel east four spaces.
7. Go south five spaces.
8. Travel west fifteen spaces.

Make a funny face out of your shape.

A

Mapping Skills

Basic Mapping Skills Card #18

Using Coordinates

Color the boxes:

A1 - Red
B2 - Black
D2 - Orange
C2 - Purple
A2 - Brown
C1 - Green
D1 - Yellow
B1 - Blue

	A	B	C	D
1				
2				

Mapping Skills

Basic Mapping Skills Card #19

Using Coordinates on a Grid

Draw a line between these points:

J 1 - B1	J1 - J10	H15 - H23	D23 - H23	A18 - 120
B 1 - B10	J1 - B10	H15 - D15	D15 - H23	A20 - D23
B10 - J10	B1 - J10	D15 - D23	D15 - A18	D15 - H23
				H15 - D23

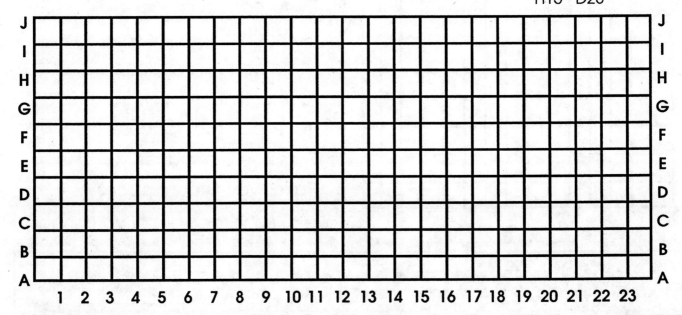

Basic Mapping Skills Card #20

Mapping to Scale

Carefully measure your classroom in meters or feet.

You are going to map your classroom to scale. You will work with a classmate.

Decide what your scale will be.

Example: 1 centimeter (cm) = 1 meter (m) or 1 inch (in) = 1 foot (ft)

Use one-centimeter or one-inch graph paper to help you plan the map. Show as many pieces of furniture (in scale) as you can.

Remember to measure carefully and do your map in pencil so it can be easily erased if you make a mistake.

Don't forget your legend, the symbols and the title.

Mapping Skills

World Mapping Skills Card #1

Our World

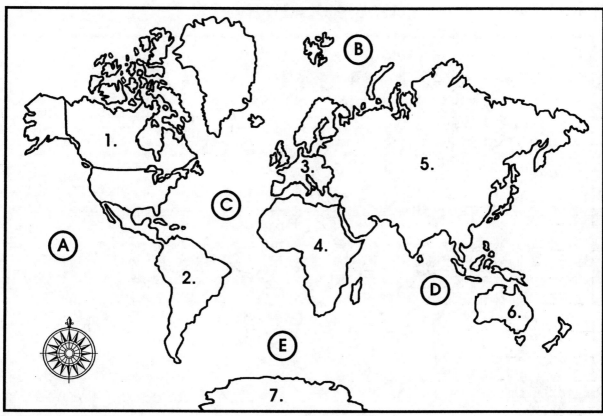

This is a map of the _____.

The world is divided into seven _____.

The continents are:

1. _____
2. _____
3. _____
4. _____

5. _____
6. _____
7. _____

Color each continent a different color.

In the world there are five _____.

The oceans are:

a) _____
b) _____
c) _____

d) _____
e) _____

Color the waters blue.

Mapping Skills

World Mapping Skills Card #2

Where Do We Live?

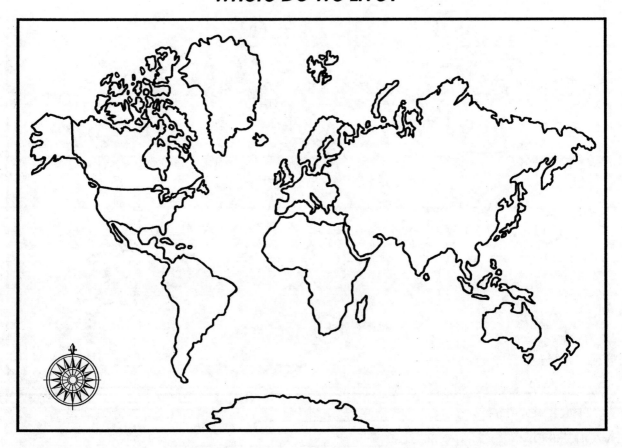

We live in the country called _____. It is located on the

continent called _____. There are _____

countries in North America. They are _____, the

_____ and _____.

On the east coast is found the _____. On the west coast

is found the _____.

Color Canada red, the United States yellow, and Mexico green.

The continent of North America is found in the _____.

Mapping Skills

World Mapping Skills Card #3

Reading the Map of North America

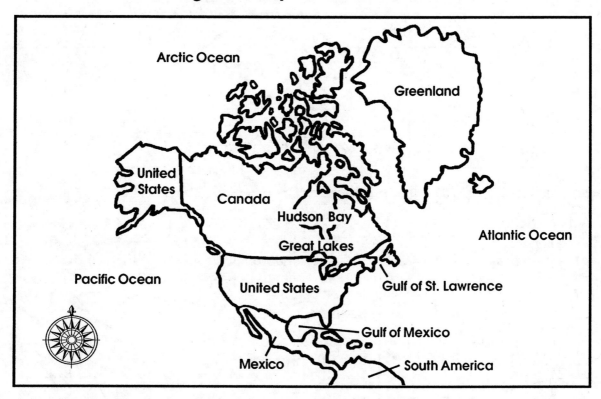

Complete the following sentences by choosing words from the map.

1. The continent shown on the map is _____.

2. The ocean east of North America is the _____.

3. The ocean north of North America is the _____.

4. The ocean west of North America is the _____.

5. _____ is the largest island.

6. Most of the islands in the north belong to _____.

7. The Great Lakes are part of the boundary between _____ and the _____.

8. The country of _____ is found south of the United States.

9. The Gulf of St. Lawrence and the Gulf of Mexico are two large bodies of _____ _____.

10. Hudson Bay reaches into the country of _____.

Mapping Skills

World Mapping Skills Card #4

Reading the Map of Canada

This is a _____ map of Canada. A political map shows

_____ and _____ between the _____,

_____, _____, and _____.

1. List the names of Canada's ten provinces and three territories in column A.
   List their capital cities in column B.

Column A	Column B
_____	_____
_____	_____

_____   _____
_____   _____
_____   _____
_____   _____
_____   _____
_____   _____
_____   _____
_____   _____
_____   _____
_____   _____

2. Which five areas in Canada do not share any of their border with the United States?

_____
_____
_____

3. Which body of water lies directly north of Canada? _____ west of Canada? _____ east of Canada? _____

4. Which area in Canada has the most islands? _____

5. What is the name of Canada's closest neighbor? _____

6. What is the name of the capital city of Canada? _____ In which province is it located? _____

7. Which province is an island? _____

8. Which province is an island and part of the mainland? _____

9. Which two provinces do not have any water as a border or boundary?

_____

10. Which American state is west of the Yukon? _____

11. Which provincial capital city is located on an island in western Canada? _____ In which province is it found? _____

12. What are the names of the three prairie provinces?

_____

13. What are the names of the atlantic provinces? _____

_____
_____

Mapping Skills

World Mapping Skills Card #5

Reading a Map of the United States

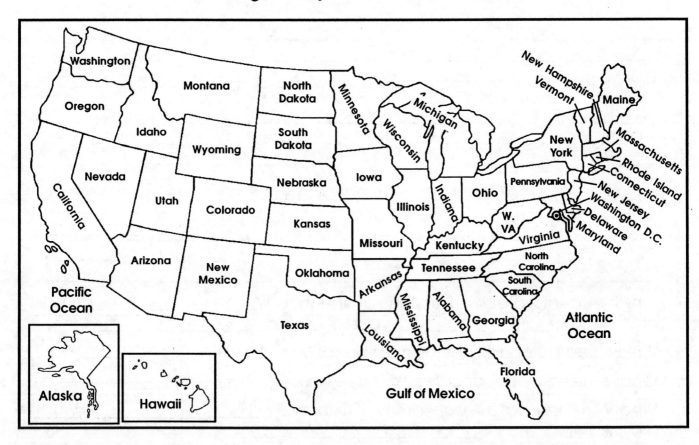

Look at the map of the United States carefully. Locate the answers to complete the sentences or to answer the questions that refer to this map.

1. The United States is also located in the continent of _____.

2. It is located between the countries of _____ and _____.

3. The United States is made up of _____ states and the District of Columbia.

4. What are the names of the states located on the west coast of the United States?

_____

 # Mapping Skills

5. What are the names of the states that border on the Gulf of Mexico?

_____

_____

6. Which states border the country of Canada?

_____

_____

_____

7. What are the names of the three rivers that are tributaries of the Mississippi River?

_____

_____

8. Which river forms part of the boundary between the United States and Mexico?

_____

9. Which two states are not connected to the United States physically?

_____

10. Which state is located the farthest south? _____

11. Which state is the farthest north? _____

12. Which two states are separated by one of the Great Lakes?

_____

13. What is the name of the capital city of the United States? _____

14. Which state is a long peninsula? _____

15. Which state is made up of a group of islands that vary in size and shape? _____

16. Make a list of the names of the states that you have visited.

_____

_____

Mapping Skills

World Mapping Skills Card #6

Labeling a Map

1. Obtain a map of the world from your teacher.

2. Using an atlas locate your country on a world map. Color it **green** on your world map.

3. Put a directional indicator on the map.

4. Locate the following oceans and neatly print their names on your world map.

   Atlantic Ocean   Indian Ocean
   Pacific Ocean   Southern Ocean
   Arctic Ocean

5. Choose the names of **ten** countries that you have heard about. Make a list of their names on the lines below.

   _____

   _____

   Now locate them on a world map. Label them neatly on the map. Be sure to print their names.

6. Which of those ten countries is the closest to your country?

   _____

7. Which of those ten countries are the farthest away?

   _____

8. How would you color your map? What color would the land be? What color will you make the the water?

   Discuss with your teacher and decide which colors you will need.

   Do you need a legend?

   What symbols will you use in your legend and on the map?

   Be sure to label your map neatly.

Mapping Skills

World Mapping Skills Card #7

Locating Places on a Map

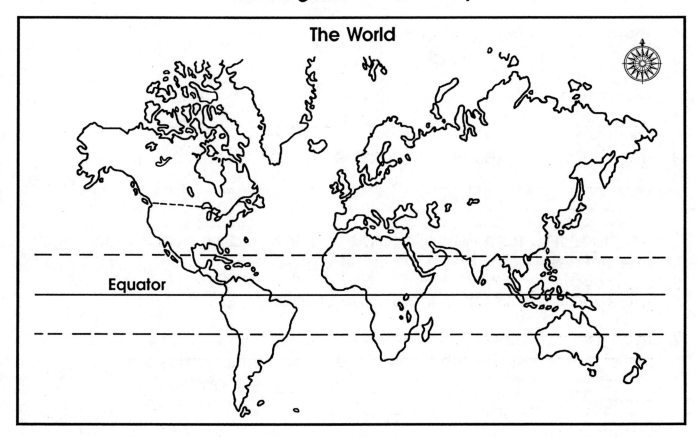

The World

Equator

Since the world map shows so many places, it is not always easy to locate something using only a directional indicator.

Cartographers decided a long time ago to use **imaginary** lines to help people when they read maps of the world.

On the map above, you will see three lines drawn across the world map. The center, solid line, is called the **equator**. It divides the world in half.

Countries above the equator are said to be "north of the equator", while countries below the equator are said to be "south of the equator".

Using an atlas and the world map above, complete the activities on the accompanying page.

 # Mapping Skills

1. Two countries that are **north** of the equator are _____ and _____.

2. Three countries that are **south** of the equator are _____, _____ and _____.

3. Name two countries that "touch" or lie along the equator. _____ and _____

4. The equator passes over three, large oceans. They are the _____, the _____ and the _____.

5. If a plane flew from Australia to Mexico, it would go over the equator. **True** or **False**

6. The equator passes over India. **True** or **False**

7. There are two broken lines shown on this world map. One lies north of the equator and the other lies to the south. Their names are the _____ and the _____.

8. Print their names on the broken lines in blue pencil.

9. Canada is found _____ of the Tropic of Cancer.

10. The Tropic of Capricorn passes through three continents. What are their names?
_____
_____

11. Australia is located _____ of the equator.

12. What are the names of the four continents that are north of the Tropic of Cancer?
_____
_____

Mapping Skills

World Mapping Skills Card #8

Locating Places on a Map

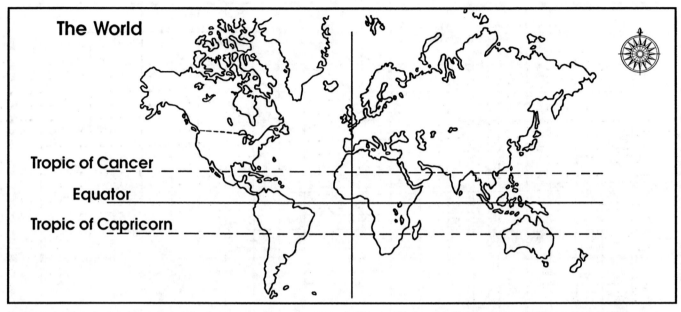

The World

Tropic of Cancer

Equator

Tropic of Capricorn

In order to make maps even easier to read, cartographers decided to put another imaginary line on the map of the world. This line has a special name. It is called the **prime meridian**.

All places in the world are either east or west of the prime meridian.

Print the word prime meridian in green along the line on the map.

Complete the following activities using the map.

1. Three countries that are east of the prime meridian are _____, _____ and _____.

2. Two countries that are west of the prime meridian are _____ and _____.

3. Name two countries that are north of the equator and east of the prime meridian. _____

4. Name two countries that are south of the equator and west of the prime meridian. _____ _____

5. Australia is _____ of the equator and _____ of the prime meridian.

6. Mexico is _____ of the equator and _____ of the prime meridian.

Locating Countries Using Coordinates

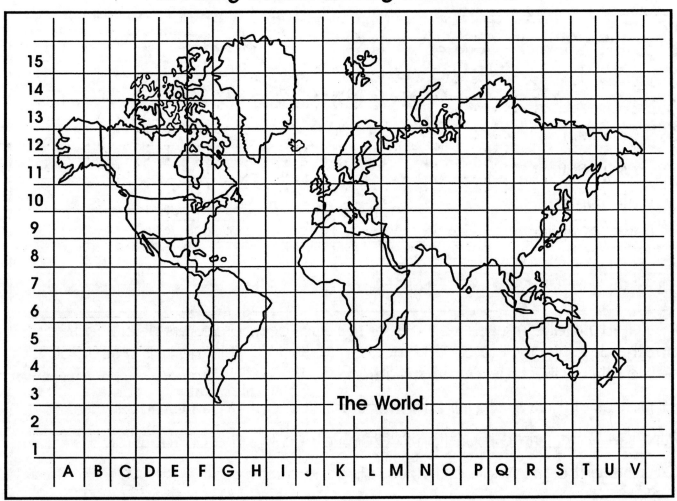

The World

Another way to locate countries or bodies of water is to divide up the world map as you see above. This is called a **grid**.

Put your finger on the letter **S** and move it up until it rests across from the number **5**.

Your finger is resting on Australia. That part of Australia is located at the coordinates of **S,5**.

Using this map, and a map of countries, locate land and/or bodies of water to answer the activities on the following page.

Mapping Skills

1. Use the coordinates below to locate a country or a body of water. Print its name on the line beside the coordinates.

   a) H,13 _____

   b) P,11 _____

   c) E,11 _____

   d) D,9 _____

   e) 0,6 _____

   f) U,4 _____

   g) H,6 _____

   h) 1,9 _____

   i) C,4 _____

   j) M,14 _____

   k) E,8 _____

   l) S,5 _____

2. Listed below are the names of countries found on a world map. Beside each one write the coordinates.

   a) Egypt _____

   b) France _____

   c) United States _____

   d) Canada _____

   e) India _____

   f) Mexico _____

   g) British Isles _____

   h) Africa _____

   i) Japan _____

   k) China _____

3. Although this method of locating countries or bodies of water is a good one, what problems might one have in using this method?

   _____

   _____

   _____

   _____

   _____

   _____

   _____

   _____

   _____

Mapping Skills

World Mapping Skills Card #10

Using Latitude and Longitude

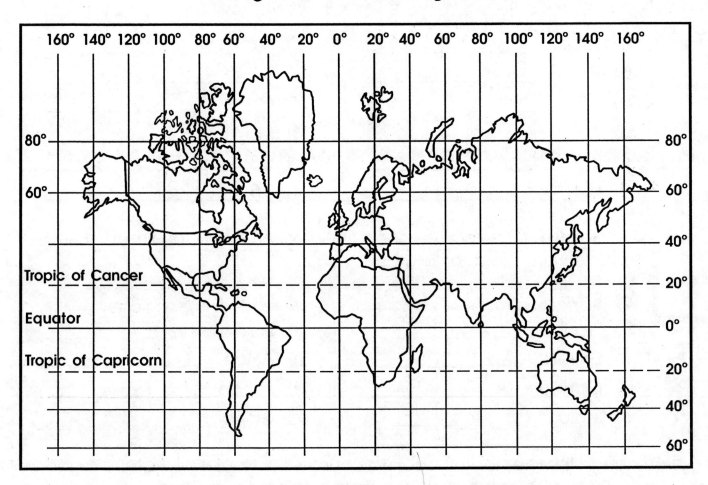

This is a map of the world that you would usually see in a student atlas.

It has the equator, Tropic of Cancer, Tropic of Capricorn and the prime meridian marked on it.

In addition, it also has other lines as well.

The lines that run the same way as the equator are called **parallels of latitude**.

The lines that run the same direction as the prime meridian are called **meridians of longitude**.

We usually call these lines just **latitude** and **longitude**.

Mapping Skills

All atlases are marked exactly the same way. The positions of the longitude and latitude lines **never change**.

If you wanted to tell someone where Greenland could be found in terms of latitude and longitude, you could say this:

"Greenland is north of the equator at about 80^0 latitude, and west of the prime meridian at about 40^0 longitude."

Or

you could just say, "80^0 N, 40^0 W".

1. Below are some coordinates of countries or bodies of water using latitude and longitude. Use your school atlas to identify each one.

   a) 20^0 N, 40^0 W _____

   b) 40^0 N, 100^0 W _____

   c) 60^0 N, 80^0 E _____

   d) 60^0 N, 140^0 E _____

   e) 0^0 N, 80^0 E _____

   f) 60^0 N, 100^0 W _____

2. Countries are big and can have their area spread over many coordinates. Write the coordinates in latitude and longitude that you think are proper for these countries.

   a) Australia _____

   b) China _____

   c) Mexico _____

   d) France _____

   e) Iceland _____

   f) New Zealand _____

Mapping Skills

Mapping Word Study Card #1

Look for the Worldly Words

Find the words in the word search map that pertain to mapping terms.

Circle each one that you are able to locate.

```
A M D Y Q A H D J W A Q F V P Q E A B Z O P Q Y I J
O I C O N T I N E N T S X P M O U N O M C R F H P G
K B O Z E N W I Q E Y G L T T R N D L A T I T U D E
N T M L F B R C U H R B K Z L S M D E N W M L X U K
R G P V H F G Y A K I J S T U C V G L O B E R V S W
O W A N O F O R T T K Y H R X I C Z R F B M A P V M
C Z S C C B L N O R T H P O L E S J A Q G E N W T X
I D S V E U S A R G Q Z J P I D H T E K Y R L P O U
R A R B A C A D P R C P P I T O A E Z R J I P G O H
P C O U N T R I E S Q J B C N B Y W L F Q D B M I K
A A S V S E C F E D U O S O U T H P O L E I L J F W
C R E N U W T I M F I K S F R A X G N S C A Y L N M
F D X L G A I D G G N S Q C U W M D G H D N E K N X
O I Q T C H C K E J H V L A X I S I I J B I X P V O
C N R J Z B C I L F H V T N Y Z L X T Q S W U Z D A
I A A R C T I C K B I H Q C F N U I U V K C U H Y E
P L D Z Q G R I D J G T R E O C G W D L R P A V C Z
O V F U L S C L O D N E R R S J T V E X M S W L F A
R I G N X P L E M P F Q S P D A H M X U T Q R G E A
T M W K O H E M I S P H E R E Z K Y L N T O Y S Z B
```

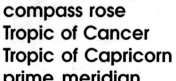

compass rose	continents	grid	North Pole
Tropic of Cancer	countries	oceans	Arctic Circle
Tropic of Capricorn	hemisphere	map	South Pole
prime meridian	longitude	axis	latitude
cardinal	scale	globe	equator

 OTM-107 • SSA1-07 Mapping Skills

Mapping Skills

Mapping Word Study Card #2

Land Form Crossword Fun!

In the world there are many land forms. Read each crossword puzzle clue carefully and complete the puzzle.

Across:

2. an area of land completely surrounded by water
4. an unusually high elevation that rises steeply
6. the land bordering the sea
7. a body of fresh water
10. a large stream of fresh water
11. a long, narrow land area that lies between two mountains or hills
12. an arm of an ocean, sea or lake extending into land

Down:

1. a large, treeless, flat land
2. a narrow strip of land between two bodies of water, connecting two large land areas
3. a narrow, man-made waterway used by boats
5. a river or stream that flows into a larger stream or other body of water
8. a narrow body of water connecting two larger bodies of water
9. a triangular area of soil at the mouth of a river

Answer Key

What is a Map?: *(page 17)*
Paragraph 1: map, picture, earth, diagram, city, country, continent, world
Paragraph 2: land, water, roads, buildings, trees, flat

3. Canada   4. west coast   5. North America
6. Alaska, United States, Alberta

1. Maps are used to find places, measure distances, plan trips and holidays, find the way to places, navigate the ocean and the air, and gain information about a place.
2. Certain maps tell us the population of a country and its location;the climate of a country; transportation routes; where minerals are located; the types of vegetation and location; the types of physical features and their location; where crops are grown; where livestock is raised; where countries are located; the location of oceans, seas, rivers and lakes; areas that receive different amounts of rainfall; where animals live; etc.
3. Cartography is the study and the making of maps.
4. A cartographer is a person who makes maps.

Kinds of Maps: *(page 18)*
1. a) general reference maps; mobility maps; thematic maps
2. a) political boundaries or borders
   b) geographic features   c) bodies of water
   d) cities and towns

   a) maps of provinces and states
   b) maps of countries   c) maps of continents
   d) maps of the world
3. They are usually found in atlases.
4. A political map is one that emphasizes the boundaries of countries, provinces, states and counties.
5. A physical or relief map emphasizes the location of physical features found on the earth's surface such as mountains, valleys, rivers and lakes.

Mobility Maps: *(page 19)*
1. A mobility map is one that helps people find their way from one place to another.
2. They are used for travel on land, on water, and in the air.
3. A chart is a type of map that shows the ocean depths and dangerous underwater rocks. Star charts show the positions of the stars in the sky.
4. Pilots and ship captains use charts to navigate the air and oceans by plane and ship.
5. A road map is the most common mobility map.
6. • different types of roads and highways
   • the location of cities and towns
   • the location of state or provincial parks
   • the location of lakes and rivers
7. street maps, city maps, transit maps, nautical charts, aeronautical charts, county maps, community maps

Thematic Maps: *(page 20)*
1. A thematic map focuses on one particular feature of a country or place.

   natural resources, vegetation areas, population, types of soil, major products, location of minerals, climate, precipitation, temperature, physical features

Inventory Maps: *(page 20)*
1. An inventory map is similar to a thematic map but is more precise. It concentrates on a specific feature. A map that shows every building in a city or community is an inventory map.

Directional Indicators - Part A: *(page 21)*
compass, direction, round, glass-covered, needle, north, north, east, south, west, cardinal, points, intermediate, northeast, southeast, southwest, northwest

a) northeast, north, east   b) southeast
c) northwest   d) southwest

Directional Indicators - Part B: *(page 22)*
map, compass rose, cardinal, north, east, south, west, north, south, east, west

1. north   2. east   3. southwest
4. northwest   5. southeast   6. northeast
7. south   8. west, top, north

Map Symbols: *(page 23)*
symbol, drawings, maps, represents, easily, legend, key, information, opens, legend

Map Symbols Used in Atlases: *(page 24)*
1. international boundary   2. other boundary
3. capital city of a country   4. other capital
5. city or town   6. river
7. seasonal river   8. mountain peak
9. mountain pass   10. bridge
11. lake   12. seasonal lake
13. Dry Lake   14. canal
15. swamp   16. desert
17. ruins   18. roads
19. highway numbers   20. railroad

A Map Tells Distance: *(page 24)*
bar scale, ruler, measuring tape, long
Scale means size. Drawing or making anything to scale means to make a copy which is exactly like the real thing except for size.

scale, drawings, large, centimeter (inch), meter (yard) kilometer (mile)

What is a Globe?: *(page 25)*
globe, earth, roundness, world, stand, spin, rotates
map, pasted, printed, sphere, terrestrial
triangular, gores, world map, lands, seas, shapes, positions

How are Globes Used: *(page 26)*
1. • in the study of geography
   • to help plan air and sea routes
   • in establishing satellite communications
2. It gives a true picture of the earth as a whole. A globe represents all parts of the earth's surface true to scale. Distances, areas and directions are not distorted as they are on flat maps.

Hemispheres: *(page 26)*
1. A hemisphere is one-half of a sphere. It is a name given to any half of the globe.
2. The globe is divided into four main hemispheres.
3. the northern and southern hemispheres, the eastern and western hemispheres, the land and water hemispheres, the daylight and darkness hemispheres

The Northern and Southern Hemispheres: *(page 26)*
equator, boundary, north, northern, south, southern
  A) northern hemisphere   B) southern hemisphere

The Eastern and Western Hemispheres: *(page 27)*
natural, dividing, line, Europe, Asia, Africa, Australia, North America, South America
  A) eastern hemisphere   B) western hemisphere

Land and Water Hemispheres: *(page 27)*
half, most, London, England, water, water hemisphere, New Zealand

Daylight and Darkness Hemispheres: *(page 27)*
daylight, darkness, boundary, line, twilight, dusk, dawn, rotates

Lines on the Globe: *(page 27)*
Geographic grids, lines, locate, parallels, latitude, meridians, lines, longitude, east, west, equator, degrees, earth's poles, equator, zero, degrees, 90⁰, North, 90⁰, South, Degrees, 60, longitude, meridians, Greenwich, prime, meridian, north, south, meet, decreases

Parallels of Latitude: *(page 28)*
  1. Arctic Circle   2. Tropic of Cancer
  3. Equator   4. Tropic of Capricorn
  5. Antarctic Circle

Day and Night: *(page 29)*
solar, earth, Day, sun, Night, dark, away
midnight, two, twelve, midnight, noon, a.m., noon, midnight, p.m.
daylight, tilt, axis, pole, slant, North, South, dark, away, dark, sunlight

The Seasons: *(page 29)*
four, spring, summer, autumn, winter, three, temperature, weather, length of daylight,
warmer, longer, hot, warm,
cooler, shorten, cold, shorter
changing, position, North Pole, northern, most, least, winter, starts, autumn
June 21, solstice, longest, winter, December 21, shortest, spring, March 21, September 21, 22, 12, sunlight, 12, darkness

Basic Mapping Skills Card #1: *(page 30)*
Symbols should be colored as instructed.

Basic Mapping Skills Card #2: *(page 31)*
  1. west   2. east   3. south   4. south
  5. north   6. west, road

Basic Mapping Skills Card #3: *(page 32)*
Streets should be colored as indicated.

Basic Mapping Skills Card#4: *(page 32)*
  1. east   2. south
  3. east, Spirit Town, Gremlin City
  4. south   5. north

Basic Mapping Skills Card #5: *(page 33)*
  1. north   2. Royal, Queen
  3. Royal Avenue   4. Elizabeth Avenue
  5. north, south, east   6. library
  7. Royal Avenue   8. east, west
  9. market, meat shop   10. King, Royal

Basic Mapping Skills Card #6: *(page 34)*
Map must contain all the symbols as directed.

Basic Mapping Skills Card #7: *(page 35)*
  1. bridge   2. mountains   3. lake
  4. boundary line 5. river   6. railroad
  7. highway   8. city

Basic Mapping Skills Card #8: *(page 35)*
The map must contain all the features indicated in the instructions.

Basic Mapping Skills Card #9: *(page 36)*
The map must be completed as indicated in the instructions.

Basic Mapping Skills Card #10: *(page 37)*
The map must be completed as indicated in the instructions.

Basic Mapping Skills Card #11 to 13: *(page 38)*
Answers may vary.

Basic Mapping Skills Card #14: *(page 41)*
13 cm; 65 km
  1. 25   2. 40   3. 55   4. 40
  5. Answers may vary.

Basic Mapping Skills Card #15: *(page 42)*
Answers may vary.

Basic Mapping Skills Card #16: (page 42)
Pictures should be accurately done.

Basic Mapping Skills Card #17: *(page 43)*
Directions must be followed accurately.

Basic Mapping Skills Card #18: *(page 43)*
Coloring must be done correctly.

Basic Mapping Skills Card #19: *(page 44)*
Two shapes will be made.

Basic Mapping Skills Card #20: *(page 44)*
Answers may vary.

World Mapping Skills Card #1: *(page 45)*
world, continents
  1. North America   2. South America   3. Europe
  4. Africa   5. Asia   6. Australia
  7. Antarctica, oceans

  a) Pacific Ocean   b) Arctic Ocean
  c) Atlantic Ocean   d) Indian Ocean
  e) Southern Ocean

World Mapping Skills Card #2: *(page 46)*
Canada, North America, three, Canada, United States, Mexico, Atlantic Ocean, Pacific Ocean, countries should be colored as indicated, Western Hemisphere

World Mapping Skills Card #3: *(page 47)*
  1. North America   2. Atlantic Ocean
  3. Arctic Ocean   4. Pacific Ocean
  5. Greenland   6. Canada
  7. Canada, United States 8. Mexico
  9. salt water   10. Canada

World Mapping Skills Card #4: *(page 48)*
political, borders, boundaries, provinces, territories, states, countries

  1. Prince Edward Island - Charlottetown, Newfoundland and Labrador - St. John's, Nova Scotia - Halifax, New Brunswick - Fredericton, Québec - Québec City, Ontario - Toronto, Manitoba - Winnipeg, Saskatchewan - Regina, Alberta - Edmonton, British Columbia - Victoria, Yukon - Whitehorse, Northwest Territories - Yellowknife, Nunavut - Iqaluit

2. Prince Edward Island, Newfoundland and Labrador, Nova Scotia, Nunavut, Northwest Territories
3. Arctic Ocean, Pacific Ocean, Atlantic Ocean   4. Nunavut
5. the United States   6. Ottawa, Ontario
7. Prince Edward Island   8. Newfoundland and Labrador
9. Saskatchewan, Alberta   10. Alaska
11. Victoria, British Columbia   12. Manitoba, Saskatchewan, Alberta
13. Nova Scotia, Newfoundland, New Brunswick, Prince Edward Island

World Mapping Skills Card #5: *(page 50)*
1. North America   2. Canada, Mexico   3. 50
4. Washington, Oregon, California, Alaska   5. Texas, Louisiana, Mississippi, Alabama, Florida
6. Alaska, Washington, Idaho, Montana, North Dakota, Minnesota, Michigan, New York, Vermont, New Hampshire, Maine
7. Arkansas River, Missouri River, Ohio River   8. Rio Grande   9. Alaska, Hawaii
10. Hawaii   11. Alaska   12. Wisconsin and Michigan
13. Washington   14. Florida   15. Hawaii
16. Answers may vary.

World Mapping Skills Card #6: *(page 52)*
Answers may vary.

World Mapping Skills Card #7: *(page 53)*
1, 2 and 3. Answers may vary.   4. Pacific Ocean, Atlantic Ocean, Indian Ocean
5. True   6. False
7. Tropic of Cancer, Tropic of Capricorn   8. Names printed on map
9. North   10. South America, Africa, Australia
11. south   12. North America, Asia, Europe, Africa

World Mapping Skills Card #8: *(page 55)*
1, 2. Answers may vary.   3. Canada, United States
4. Africa, Australia, New Zealand   5. south, west   6. north, east

World Mapping Skills Card #9: *(page 56)*
1. a) Greenland   b) Russia   c) Canada   d) United States   e) Indian Ocean
    f) New Zealand   g) South America   h) Atlantic Ocean   i) Pacific Ocean   j) Arctic Ocean
    k) Mexico   l) Australia
2. Answers will vary.   3. Answers may vary.

World Mapping Skills Card #10: *(page 58)*
1. a) Atlantic Ocean   b) United States   c) Russia   d) Russia   e) Indian Ocean
    f) Canada   2. Allow some variance in coordinates that students give.

    a) 20^0S, 140^0E   b) 30^0N, 100^0E   c) 20^0N, 100^0W   d) 40^0N, 0^0 e) 70^0N, 20^0W
    f) 40^0S, 180^0E (approx.)

Mapping Word Study Card #1: *(page 60)*

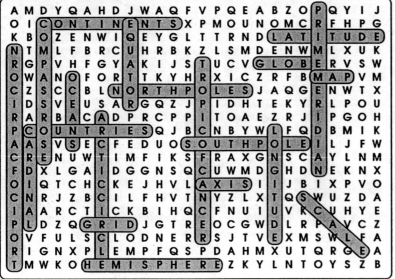

Mapping Word Study Card #2: *(page 61)*

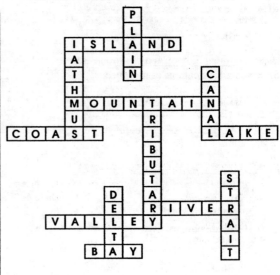